The Aeroplane
Trial Flight Guide

Congratulations!

This is your first step into the wonderful
World of Aviation.

Your personal invitation to experience the
pleasure of being airborne.

Dorothy Pooley

Nothing in this manual supersedes any legislation, rules, regulations or procedures contained in any operational document issued by Her Majesty's Stationery Office, the Civil Aviation Authority, the Joint Aviation Authorities, ICAO, the manufacturers of aircraft, engines and systems, or by the operators of aircraft throughout the world.

The Trial Flight Guide (Aeroplanes) - Dorothy Pooley

Copyright 2002 © Pooleys Flight Equipment Ltd

First Edition 2002
Second Edition with amendments 2005
Third Edition 2007
Reprint with amendments 2010

ISBN: 978-1-84336-045-2

Pooleys Flight Equipment Ltd
Elstree Aerodrome
Hertfordshire
WD6 3AW
England

Tel: 0208 953 4870
Fax: 0208 953 2512
www.pooleys.com

Author — **Dorothy Pooley**

Dorothy Pooley took her first flying lesson in August 1988. She was hooked! After gaining her private licence in 1989, she continued to qualify for further ratings and finally became a flying instructor in 1992. Passionate about aviation and a dedicated educator, she now trains flying instructors and is an examiner of private pilots and instructors. Futhermore she is a helicopter instructor. Additionally, she spent many years as an aviation solicitor, providing consultancy services on a wide range of aviation matters. She is the editor and author of many articles, training manuals and books.

Since 1994 Dorothy has been an active member of the Guild of Air Pilots and Air Navigators of London, where she is the Vice-Chairman of the Education and Training Committee. She also chairs the Professional Flying Instructors Association.

In her spare time Dorothy likes to swim, cycle, ski and snorkel. She also enjoys classical music, opera and fine wine.

Nicholas Chan Editors

Nick obtained his PPL in 1998. He was then successful in winning the highly sought-after Somers Award, a scholarship administered by the Guild of Air Pilots and Air Navigators. This enabled Nick to study for and gain his Airline Transport Pilot's Licence, which he completed in March 2001. Whilst waiting for an airline job Nick studied for his flying instructor rating with Dorothy Pooley, where he displayed his talent for illustration and design, assisting Dorothy to improve the presentation of her Pre-flight briefings. He was a natural choice to illustrate this publication and was responsible for most of the photography. Nick is now flying the 767/757 with British Airways.

Shaun McConnell

Shaun is a Flight Instructor and IRI. He began flying in 2000, although his involvement in teaching started in 1993 when he became a scuba-diving instructor. Shaun also has instructor qualifications in power boat handling and first aid. He graduated in 1980 with B. Eng (hons) in Mechanical Engineering and and initially followed a career in IT, encompassing programming, software engineering, management, project management, service development and large account management. As well as teaching flying full-time, he is engaged in writing and editing aviation training books and presentations. Shaun is now flying the Dash 8 Q-400 for Flybe.

Daljeet Gill

Daljeet is Head of Design & Development for Pooleys Flight Equipment and editor of the Pooleys Private Pilots Guides, Pre-flight Briefing, R/T Communications, Pooleys ATPL Manuals and Air Presentation, Ground School Training Transparencies plus many others. Daljeet has been involved with editing, typesetting and design for all these publications. Graduated in 1999 with a BA (hons) in Graphic Design, she deals with marketing, advertising & design of our new products. She maintains our website and produces our Pooleys Catalogue annually.

Acknowledgments

This little book could not have been made possible without the help and support of the following people, to whom the author is extremely grateful:

Phil Baxter at Redhill and Maggie Smith at Shoreham for their proof-reading and helpful suggestions to improve the draft.

Introduction

Whether or not the trial lesson you have booked is a gift or you have decided to find out about flying for yourself, you will find that the experience will be greatly enhanced if you have read through this short guide in advance.

However if this book was given to you after your flight (some flying schools may do this), do not worry! You will still find that reading it will answer most, if not all of the questions which have occurred to you after your lesson.

You do not need to learn the contents of this guide, but you will find that some of the terminology and jargon will be less of a mystery when your instructor 'briefs' you for the lesson. Take a few minutes to review the contents and then go and enjoy what will surely be the first of many happy hours aloft!

Contents

So what is this Trial Lesson?

Questions!

If you have received a voucher for a Trial flying lesson, you may be wondering what to expect when you book and arrive for the lesson. What will happen? What will you have to wear? Will it be noisy or uncomfortable? Will you like it? How much time will it all take? Equally you may have decided that you want to learn to fly, but not knowing much about what is involved, you have decided to purchase the trial lesson for yourself. This little book is designed to assist your understanding and to give you an idea about what will happen when you turn up at the flying school or club.

Trial Lesson or Pleasure Flight?

What is a trial lesson? One thing to be clear about is that it is not the same as a pleasure flight. The companies that advertise pleasure flights have to satisfy specific regulations laid down by the Civil Aviation Authority ("CAA").

The Piper Tomahawk & Cessna 152, typical 2-seat training aeroplanes

Their pilots have been trained to carry out pleasure flights and they do not necessarily have to be flight instructors. On a pleasure flight you will be flown around the local sights and landmarks but you will not handle the controls of the aircraft. The pilot will sit in the left-hand seat, which is the usual captain's position.

On a trial lesson, however short its duration, you will sit in the left hand (captain's) seat and you will be able to experience flying the aircraft and operating some of the main controls as the aircraft in which you fly will have dual controls. Your pilot will have to be a fully qualified flight instructor. Before the flight you will be briefed fully on the contents of the flight and certain safety matters, including how the seatbelt and headset work and what to do in the unlikely event of an emergency.

Afterwards you will have the opportunity to ask questions about the flight itself, how to take matters forward if you decide to learn to fly and you may be given a certificate to keep as a memento and as evidence of the flight. The introductory flight or trial lesson can count towards the hours required for a pilot's licence should you decide to undertake further training.

Airfields, Aircraft, Flying Schools & Clubs, Instructors

Where to go

Unless you elect to fly a microlight *(which is a much lighter type of machine often looking like a tricycle suspended from a flexible wing),* you will not be able to take a trial lesson at your local farm strip, as flying training on "conventional" aircraft has to be carried out from a licensed aerodrome. This is mainly for safety reasons. You can find out where your local flying school is by looking it up in "Yellow Pages", or from one of the many sites on the internet *(see suggestions at the end of this book).* Alternatively, you could contact The Aircraft Owners and Pilots Association (AOPA) *(telephone number in the appendix at the back of this book)* who will give you advice and details of the local airfield or flying school.

In addition, there are a number of specialist magazines on general sale which are aimed at private pilots. These carry details of most UK airfield and flying schools. Some magazines also have a searchable website. *(Again, refer to the end of this book for suggestions).*

Shoreham Airport

What will I be flying?

The aeroplane used for your trial lesson also have to be maintained by properly licensed engineers *(again this is a CAA qualification)* and comply with minimum standards of maintenance; this is also for your safety. There are a number of popular aircraft types used for training and you may have heard of Cessnas and Pipers. These are the names of two major manufacturers of light aeroplanes similar to Ford or Vauxhall for cars.

Does it make a difference which type you learn in? Not really, as they are all considered to be simple basic trainers. However if you are very heavy *(over about 90 kg)* or very tall i.e. over 6' 2" *(1.85 m)* you may find that the 2-seater high-winged Cessna 152 is rather cramped. You would be better off electing to fly a low winged Piper **PA38** Tomahawk *(also 2-seat but rather wider)* or the 4-seater Cessna 172 or Piper **PA28** Warrior. *(Some schools also use Katanas, Diamond Stars or Grumman AA5s or Robins - they are all pretty similar.)*

You may have seen some of these aeroplanes flying, and marvelled at how small they look. When you walk up to your aeroplane on the ground it may still appear to be very small.

Piper PA38 Tomahawk

Cessna 152

However you will notice that some parts of the aeroplane are actually taller than you, and that the wingspan is quite large!

You may also be surprised to find that the speed at which you will be flying could be as fast as 100 knots *(over 100 mph!)*

School or Club?

What is the difference between a school and a club? This is not an easy question to answer, as they come in various guises. Generally speaking a flying club may be more informal.

Cessna 152

It may rely more on part-time instructors who may not necessarily wear a uniform. It may have a strong social side and offer facilities such as a bar or restaurant. A flying school is often a dedicated training establishment with less of a social side but with the facilities for advanced flying training courses.

Ready to fly!

It may also have a dedicated ground school for theoretical training.

Often the instructors will wear a uniform and the aircraft may all be painted in matching livery. There will be a Chief Flying Instructor and some operations or reception staff. In the club, it is likely that volunteers may run the operational side of things and a committee will make decisions. In a school there will be employed staff for the operational functions and more of an organisational structure, so the prices may be a little higher than those of the club.

Your Flying Instructor

Flying instructors all have to pass a large number of exams and flying tests and to have accumulated a large number of flying hours. However they vary a lot in their experience levels. You may have one in his or her early 20s who is building flying hours with a view to joining an airline later. Or you may have a retired airline pilot or ex RAF pilot, many of whom are enthusiastic about putting back into General Aviation some of their experience and expertise. In between there are others including many people who turn to flying as a second career and decide to become "career instructors".

Do not be surprised if your instructor is a very senior one, as there are many who enjoy passing on their enthusiasm to the novices even though they may normally instruct at a more senior level!

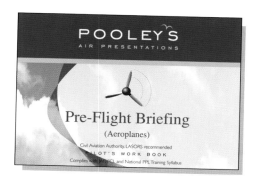

Pooleys Pre-flight Briefing, Pilot's Work Book and Powerpoint CD Rom

Before you set off for the Airfield

Is the weather suitable?

You will have complied with the instructions on the voucher and booked your lesson for a set time. It is possible that you will have been sent a briefing sheet with the voucher, but if not, you may well have been asked to phone the school before setting off to check that the weather is suitable for the lesson.

Any reputable school will not take you up in unsuitable conditions as you will not learn much and may not even enjoy the flight. It is perhaps obvious that if it is very windy or foggy then the flight will not go ahead, but there are other conditions which may not be so obvious to you. If the cloudbase is very low it will not be possible to fly, as the lesson needs to be conducted in good visual conditions. This will become clearer to you when you read the section on how the controls work. Weather that looks okay from the ground may be very hazy and unsuitable from 2000 feet up. Also weather is very localised so it may look fine where you live but be quite different 30 miles down the road. So telephone first to avoid a wasted journey. It is always possible to rebook the lesson.

Am I fit to fly?

If you are not well you should not hesitate to postpone the lesson. Any hint of a cold, a hangover or an upset stomach will be magnified at altitude and will spoil your enjoyment of the experience. If you have blocked sinuses it is potentially dangerous to fly as your ears could be damaged during the climb and the descent.

What shall I wear?

You may be wondering what to wear. It is best to wear comfortable non-restrictive clothing and avoid high-heeled shoes or boots. Non-slip soles are best. It is worth taking a sweater or jacket in winter as airfields are often windy places and you may have to walk some distance outside to reach the aeroplane. Also it is worth noting that grass airfields may be muddy so do not wear your best shoes. Aeroplanes are sometimes a bit oily or dirty so avoid that new pair of white jeans! Most light aircraft are equipped with a heater and will be almost as warm as your car but they are sometimes a bit draughty in winter. You may want to take a camera with you to record the occasion and there should be no problem taking this up in the aeroplane with you.

Finding my School

Give yourself enough time to get to the airfield and to find the school or club. At some airfields there are a large number of training organisations spread around a big area and it may take a little while to locate the correct building.

Bear in mind that if the school is busy there will be bookings all day and if you are late there may not be time to fit in your flight before the next booking. Try to give as much notice as you can if you have to cancel for any reason, as there may be a possibility of the slot being filled by someone else. The majority of instructors are paid only for the flying time and a cancellation at the last minute on a nice day is not always viewed very charitably!

Pooleys Pilot's Record & Flight Training Syllabus

At the Airfield

On Arrival

When you arrive at the school you will present your voucher to the operations or reception staff who will confirm your booking and tell you the name of the instructor. They will also tell you if there are any delays. Although they will try to keep to the schedule there are sometimes operational delays such as Air Traffic hold ups, which may unavoidably cause the instructor to run late. If that should happen, you will probably be directed to the coffee machine or café!

Paperwork and Briefings

You will probably be asked to complete a temporary membership form for insurance purposes. Then the instructor will take you to a briefing room to give you a "pre-flight briefing". For this a white board or slides may be used, together with visual aids such as wall charts and model aeroplanes although on a nice day most of this may be done at the aeroplane. If you have been able to read this book beforehand this will ensure that you derive the most benefit from the briefing. It also gives you the opportunity to ask questions which may have arisen during your reading.

After the briefing the instructor will obtain authorisation for the flight. How this occurs varies according to local procedures. It may be necessary to telephone Air Traffic Control or it may simply be a question of filling up some paperwork. Then it is out to the aeroplane!

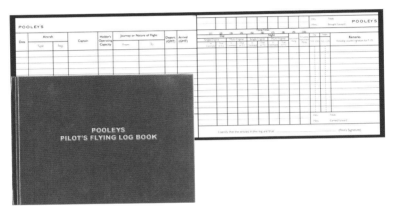

Pooleys Pilot's Flying Log Book

Pre-flight Checks

If the instructor has been using the aircraft already on that day, then he or she will probably simply check that there is sufficient fuel and oil and then help you into the aeroplane. If it is the first flight of the day then the instructor will have carried out a detailed inspection of the aeroplane. There is a legal requirement to inspect the aircraft before the first flight of each day and that should

Checking the engine oil level

reassure you about the safety of the operation. If time and circumstances permit, your instructor may well carry out this inspection with you, and explain why he/she is checking each item.

Getting on Board!

You will enter the aeroplane *(in the left hand seat)* either by climbing up onto the wing in the case of a low winged aeroplane or by entering through a small door *(avoid hitting your head on the wing!)* in the case of a Cessna. The instructor will ensure that your harness *(seatbelt)* is done up firmly across your hips and comfortably over your shoulder, before entering the aeroplane to take the right hand seat. If you are not very tall you will have been equipped with a cushion to enable you to see out. If you are uncomfortable in any way now is the time to say.

Communication in the Aeroplane

You will both be equipped with an adjustable headset and microphone to enable conversation to take place through an intercom. As well as forming an important part of the communication system, the headset also contains most of the soundproofing in the aeroplane. This saves the weight and expense of installing complex soundproofing in the aeroplane itself. The headset will not be fitted until after the instructor has started the engine, in order that any malfunctions can be heard and dealt with.

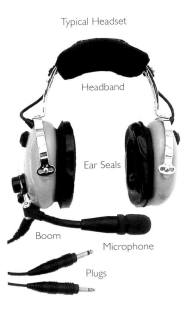

Typical Headset

Headband

Ear Seals

Boom

Microphone

Plugs

When you fit the headset, your instructor will help you to make sure that it is not so tight as to restrict you and not so loose that it will fall off. Place the microphone near your mouth. There is usually a volume control on one side of the headset, which you can adjust to the best and most comfortable level for you. You can carry on a conversation during the flight but your instructor may give you a hand signal if he has to make a radio call to the Tower or Air Traffic

Control. This is not to be interpreted as rudeness if the instructor breaks you off in mid-flow as there may be important instructions that he has to obey.

Before Take-off

The Instrument Panel

You will see in front of you a large and perhaps bewildering array of instrument dials and radios. You may have seen a similar layout if you have a flight simulator programme on your computer so some of this may be familiar to you. But if not then do read the section about the instruments and radios on pages 42 to 46.

Controls and Instrument Panel of Piper PA38

The Flying Controls

You will also see that the aeroplane is equipped with dual flying controls, a control column or yoke *(colloquially known as the "joystick")* and two rudder pedals on each side. Your instructor will show you before the aeroplane moves off from the parking area how these controls operate and which surface is moved by their operation. This may already have been done using a model during your briefing. The instructor will start the engine and carry out a few after start checks of various instruments and switches.

Radios and Air Traffic Control

Then the radio will be switched on and the instructor will call the Tower or Air Traffic Control to obtain permission to taxy the aeroplane to the "holding point", near the runway. When he speaks on the radio the instructor will indicate to you not to speak. You may notice that he has to wait for a while until the continuous stream of chatter ceases long enough for him to make the call. It is not considered good form to interrupt a radio transmission. You may not understand what is being said as in the interests of efficiency a number of special code words and abbreviations are used. Some of these are set out in the glossary at the back of this book.

Taxying to the Runway

Once he has received clearance, your instructor may invite you to place your feet lightly on the rudder pedals with your heels resting on the floor and to feel the steering of the aeroplane to the holding point. If time permits and the taxiway is not too busy, your instructor may demonstrate the steering and braking to you in more detail. He/she may then allow you to taxi the aeroplane to the holding point.

When you get there, your instructor will position the aircraft facing into wind *(this will be decided by reference to a windsock)* and will then carry out a number of checks of the engine and instruments to satisfy himself finally that the aeroplane is fully fit and safe for the flight. If there is any doubt he will explain this to you and seek the advice of an aircraft engineer. The instructor may explain to you what he is checking – feel free to ask him for more explanation.

Getting Airborne

Taking Off

Once he has received the clearance to depart, from Air Traffic Control, the instructor will manoeuvre the aeroplane onto the runway after checking the final approach path to ensure that there is no other aircraft approaching. He may ask you to place your left hand lightly on the control column or joystick to feel the movements being made during the takeoff. *("Following through on the controls").* Then he will apply full power using the throttle lever and the aeroplane will start to move forwards. You will be surprised how short the takeoff run will seem, especially if you have only been used to large jet aeroplane flights before. You will feel a slight backpressure on the control column and the aircraft will gently become airborne! You are flying! The air near the ground can often be a little turbulent as the wind swirls around but do not be alarmed, this is usual and it generally becomes smoother at altitude.

Piper PA38 Tomahawk lining up to depart

In Flight

Climbing Out

Your instructor will climb the aeroplane away from the "circuit" *(the busy traffic area around the airfield)* and may then steer the aeroplane out towards where you live *(if practical)* so that you can view your house from the air. Once a suitable altitude has been reached *(usually about 2000 feet above ground level)*, the instructor will level the aeroplane and set the power *(throttle)* to a cruise setting. You will now find that your view out to the front has improved greatly compared to the view in the climb. Now the lesson will begin. The instructor will ask you once again to follow-through on the controls so that you can feel how much pressure or movement is being applied to each control in turn. You will be surprised how little movement or pressure is required.

Attitude!

Rather than looking at the instruments your instructor will encourage you to look outside and to note the position of the horizon in relation to the upper edge of the instrument panel *(coaming)*. He will refer to this as the "attitude" of the aeroplane. It is important to notice this "picture" as you look out because this is the reference for the changes you will see. You will then note the movement of the aeroplane's nose relative to the horizon as you operate the controls.

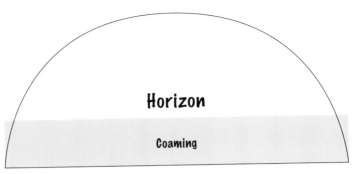

Horizon

Coaming

Normal Attitude

You may then be asked to glance at the altimeter or airspeed indicator to note changes. After each demonstration the instructor will pass control to so that you can try out the manoeuvre yourself.

Pitch: The Elevator

You will soon find out that if you apply backpressure to the control column or wheel *(it causes the elevator - the moving surface on the back of the tailplane - to tilt up)* the nose of the aeroplane will **pitch** up. Conversely when you apply forward pressure the reverse occurs and the nose will **pitch** down. The aeroplane pitches around its "lateral" *(wingtip-to-wingtip)* axis.

Pitch

Lateral axis

Roll: The Ailerons

When you rotate the control column to the left, the aeroplane will **roll** (bank) to the left and when you rotate the column to the right the aircraft will **roll** (bank) to the right. Centralising the control column with the aeroplane in the selected attitude allows the aeroplane to remain "banked" left or right. Once a bank angle has been selected you will also see the aeroplane starting to change direction as it "slips" into a turn. The aeroplane rolls around its "longitudinal" (nose-to-tail) axis.

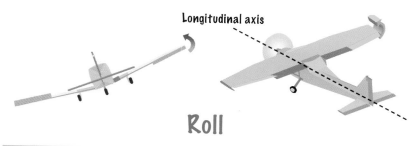

Longitudinal axis

Roll

Yaw: The Rudder

You will be shown how the **rudder** works. By pressing the left rudder pedal you will cause the aeroplane to **yaw** to the left. You will see the nose of the aeroplane move to the left, relative to distant object (or cloud). The aeroplane yaws around its "normal" (top-to-bottom) axis. As the aeroplane yaws to the left it will also begin to roll to the left and change direction as it "skids" into a turn. (If you press the right rudder pedal the aeroplane will yaw to the right and the opposite process will occur).

This may feel a little uncomfortable and is not the desired way to change direction! In practice the rudder is used to "balance" the aeroplane to prevent unwanted yaw and ensure that the aeroplane neither slips nor skids.

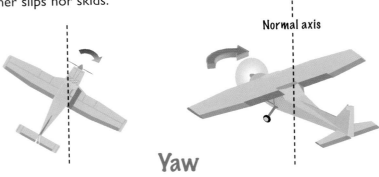

Normal axis

Yaw

Airspeed and Slipstream

After you have had an opportunity to practise pitching, rolling and yawing the aeroplane, then if time permits, your instructor may demonstrate to you the effects of airspeed and slipstream. *(Slipstream is the effect of the airflow generated by the propeller as it washes over the surfaces of the aeroplane).* You will follow through once again and can note how the controls feel much firmer and more responsive at a higher airspeed and much less responsive at a low airspeed. The instructor will fly the aeroplane at different air-speeds by pitching the aeroplane to a higher or lower nose attitude. Similarly you may note how more, or less slipstream affects the ele-vator and rudder, but the ailerons are comparatively less affected, being outside the slipstream.

Slipstream

A Longer Lesson?

How many things the instructor will demonstrate will depend on the length of time booked for the lesson. If you have only booked for 30 minutes there will not be time to show you everything but in an hour you may also be shown how to trim the aeroplane to remove control pressures and even how to make power changes or operate the flaps.

The Landing

Then it will be back to the airfield for the landing! Many people are a bit apprehensive about this, but there is no need to be. Your instructor may invite you to follow through again so that you experience how the landing is made. You will be pleasantly surprised at how gently the aeroplane will touch down and then you will taxy clear of the runway and stop briefly to carry out after-landing checks. The aeroplane will then be taxied back to the parking area and further shut-down checks carried out for safety reasons. Then the instructor will help you out of the aeroplane, ensure that the seatbelts are stowed and you will return to the clubhouse or school building. He will debrief you on how well you performed and give you the opportunity to ask questions.

Cessna 152

Piper PA28 Warrior

Some Technical Stuff

What makes an Aeroplane fly?

This is the sort of question that children like to ask their parents, in the league of "where does the wind come from" or "why is there a rainbow"? If you studied science at school you will probably have some idea of what makes an aircraft fly, but if your education was lacking in that respect you may genuinely have no idea. Whilst it is not especially important at the stage of a trial lesson to understand the principles of flight, it does become important if you decide to go on and study for your licence. It may interest you to have some insight at this stage in which case it may be worth reading the next few pages.

Lift

The force needed to keep an aeroplane in the air is called **lift**. This is produced by forcing the air to flow over the wings. The construction of the wings is such that if you looked at the cross section through them you would see a shape as below, which is called an aerofoil section.

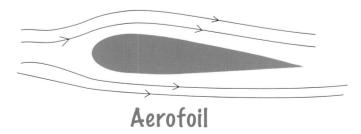

Aerofoil

This is important, as the shape causes the air flowing over the top surface of the wing to travel further and therefore faster than that passing underneath it. The faster flowing air generates an area of slightly lower pressure on the top surface and effectively the wing is "sucked" up into the lower pressure air above it. This is what holds the wing up!

Thrust

Lift is produced independently of power from the engine - this is why a glider can fly! What the engine produces is called **thrust**. The thrust is needed to get the aircraft moving along the runway in the first place and is also required to overcome drag.

Drag

Drag is the force which tries to oppose the motion of the aeroplane through the air. The presence of the aeroplane itself causes drag (you may have experienced this yourself as a child when you held your hand out of a car window as the car travelled down the road). The flow of the air over the body of the aeroplane also caused drag *(this is called "skin friction")*. In addition some of the drag is a by-product of lift itself.

Weight

The other force involved is **weight**. The weight of the aeroplane determines how much lift is required to get it into the air.

The "4 Forces"

The arrangement of these forces is shown on the diagram below. As long as the lift produced by the wings is enough to overcome the weight, and the thrust produced by the engine is enough to overcome the drag, then the aeroplane will fly. Even if the engine stops, if you allow the aeroplane to descend in a glide, the airspeed resulting will be high enough to generate sufficient lift to keep the aircraft gliding down, rather like a car coasting down a hill.

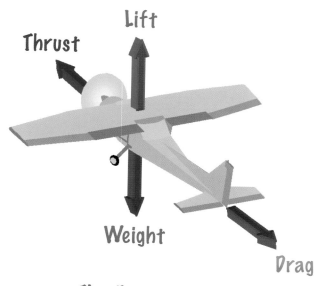

The Four Forces

1.1   Elevator

On aeroplanes such as the Cessna 152, the elevator is a hinged surface on the rear of the fixed tailplane. On some Piper aircraft *(such as the PA28)* the whole tailplane surface moves and this is called a stabilator. Applying forward pressure to the control column causes the elevator to move down and increase the lift over the tailplane. This results in the nose of the aeroplane pitching down. Conversely, applying back pressure causes the nose to pitch up.

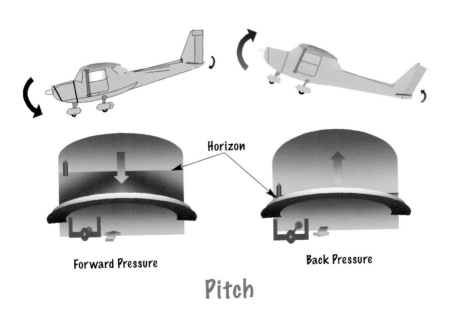

Forward Pressure   Back Pressure

Pitch

Rotating the control column to the left causes the left aileron to move up and the right aileron to move down. This results in an increase of lift on the right wing causing it to rise and the reduction of lift on the left wing causes it to lower. The aeroplane will therefore roll to the left. The reverse will occur if the control column is rotated to the right.

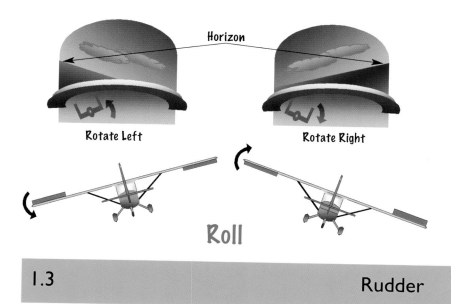

Horizon

Rotate Left   Rotate Right

Roll

1.3   Rudder

On the ground the rudder pedals are used for steering the aeroplane and to operate the brakes. During take-off and landing, your heels should be on the floor to avoid inadvertently applying the brakes. To operate the brakes you slide your feet up the pedals to pivot the top portion forwards. To turn the aeroplane on the ground, simply pressing the right pedal will turn the aeroplane right and vice versa. Applying the brake during the turn will tighten up the turn.

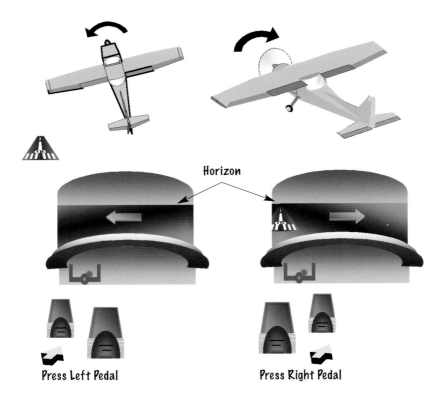

Press Left Pedal   Press Right Pedal

In flight, the rudder, hinged on the rear of the vertical tailfin, is also operated by the rudder pedals. Pressing the right rudder pedal now moves the rudder to the right, causing the aeroplane to yaw to the right. This is best observed with reference to an object or cloud in the distance. You will see the nose of the aeroplane clearly move to the right, relative to your chosen object. Pressing the left rudder pedal will cause the aeroplane to yaw to the left. This is neither a comfortable nor efficient way of making a turn and normally the rudder will be used in coordination with the ailerons to produce a "balanced" and comfortable turn.

Pooleys Demonstration Aeroplane

2.1   Throttle

This is a lever or push/pull control usually positioned in centre of the control panel or on a separate "quadrant". It works like the accelerator in your car - pressing it into the panel will increase the power and pulling it out will reduce the power. Pulling the throttle fully out does not stop the engine, simply allows it to tick over or "idle" just like a car engine.

Throttle Lever

Push/Pull Throttle Control

Throttle Types

This is another lever or push/pull control which is used to direct hot air into the carburettor intake to prevent ice from forming and blocking the intake even on a warm day. The design of a carburettor means that this problem may occur in conditions of high relative humidity or when there is a low power setting, so it is used for safety reasons and you will see your instructor using the "carb heat" regularly during the flight.

Carburettor Heat Control

Push/Pull Carburettor
Heat Control

Carburettor Heat

The mixture control is usually coloured red. If pulled fully out, the engine will stop as the fuel flow will be cut off. The lever can be used in flight to set the correct mixture of fuel and air for optimum performance from the engine. At altitude the air becomes thinner *(you may have experienced this if you have been up a mountain)* and unless this procedure is carried out the engine would not run efficiently.

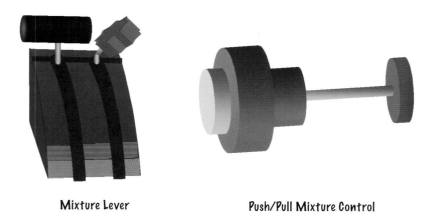

Mixture Lever   Push/Pull Mixture Control

Mixture Levers

3   Other Controls

3.1   Trim Wheel

       This is used to remove any forward or backward pressure on the control column which would otherwise make the flying tiring for the pilot. It is usually possible to trim the aeroplane "hands off" so that there is little or no input required to hold the aeroplane in the attitude set by the pilot. The trim wheel is located either in the centre of the control panel or on the floor between the front seats.

Trim Wheel

This may be an electrical switch *(as in a Cessna 152)* or a lever that looks like the handbrake in a car *(in a Piper)*. Operating the flap selector allows a section of the wing which is hinged to extend rearwards into the airflow, increasing both lift and drag. The flaps may be used during take-off under some circumstances, and will generally always be used for the landing.

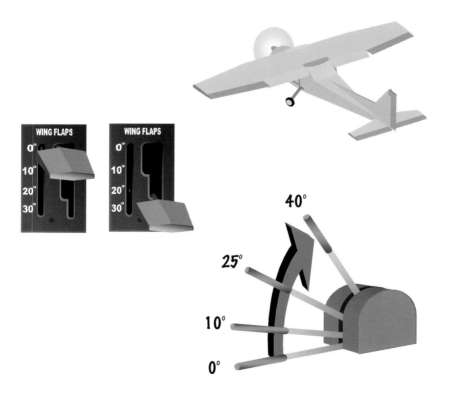

Types of Flap Lever

As previously stated these are generally operated by pressing the tops of the rudder pedals although in some older aeroplanes such as the Piper Cub, heelbrakes may be fitted. The principle is the same. There is also often a parking brake fitted. This is not often a very sophisticated system in light aircraft and should not be relied on so you will probably see your instructor "covering" the brakes with his or her feet when (s)he carries out the power checks to ensure that the aeroplane does not slip forwards.

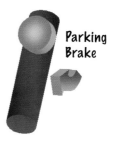

Parking Brake

Brakes

The radio is needed for communications with Air Traffic Control. This is important to obtain clearance for take-off and landing. You will hear lots of abbreviations and codes being spoken over the radio. There is a special "language" for the radio communications to ensure that valuable airtime is not wasted. Some of the abbreviations are set out in the glossary at the back of this book. You may see other radios in the aeroplane as well as the "communications" or "com" radio(s). These are known as "navigation" or "nav" radios and are used to tune into ground based radio beacons to assist with the navigation of the aeroplane. You may also recognise the GPS satellite based navigation system, if it has been fitted.

A combined communication and navigation radio

5.1   Attitude Indicator (artificial horizon)

This instrument can be used to judge the amount of pitch or bank angle being applied, but it is generally only relied on if the aeroplane is flying in cloud, by sole reference to instruments. Otherwise pitch and bank are judged by looking outside at the horizon.

5.2 Magnetic Compass & Direction Indicator

Since a compass is very sensitive and moves about a lot when the aeroplane is flying, a direction indicator ("DI") (which is a gyroscope) is usually fitted to complement the magnetic compass and show heading information. The DI has to be aligned with the magnetic compass regularly to prevent errors developing. Headings are usually worked out relative to magnetic north.

5.3 Altimeter

Subscale

This instrument is essentially a barometer which shows the pilot how high the aeroplane is, by measuring the air pressure. Different weather conditions will cause the air pressure to change, so it is necessary to set the correct sea level pressure in a sub-scale on the instrument. This will ensure that the correct reading is displayed on the dial.

5.4   Airspeed Indicator (ASI)

A pilot needs to know that the correct speed is being achieved at various stages of flight. This is particularly important for take-off, to ensure that the wings are developing sufficient lift. It is also important for the approach to land, where an airspeed much lower than cruising speed will be used. The dial usually has a colour coded system for displaying the various limits of speeds appropriate to the aircraft.

5.5   Vertical Speed Indicator (VSI)

This instrument shows rate of climb or descent in 100s of feet per minute.

5.6   Turn Coordinator & Balance Ball

Balance Ball

This is a combined instrument. It shows rate of turn of the aircraft and has a glass tube containing a ball which works a bit like a spirit level. The movement of the ball during turning manoeuvres shows slip and skid (or yaw) as the ball moves left or right in the tube, according to the forces acting on the aeroplane.

5.7   Tachometer (rpm)

This is similar to the rev-counter in your car. The green band shows the normal operating range for the aircraft when it is in the cruise.

5.8   Temperature & Pressure Gauges

These little gauges are very important for the monitoring of the health of the engine. Again, green bands will indicate the normal operating range and any deviation outside these green bands should call the pilot to question what is happening.

After the flight

Now What?

When you come back from the flight it is more than likely that you will be very excited and want to experience some more flying. If you had booked the lesson yourself to find out more about flying and this lesson decides the matter for you, then you may have already enquired into the prices of courses and familiarised yourself with the options.

However, if this was a present, you may have several questions. You can ask your instructor who will very probably be happy to give you information, but if he has to go straight off again with another student it might be best to talk to the reception or operations staff who may have handouts and printed price lists to give you.

To gain a private pilot's licence ("PPL") you will have to follow a syllabus of instruction. The legal minimum for a JAR PPL is 45 hours of flight training to include at least 25 hours dual instruction and 10 hours solo flying. You have to be 16 years old to fly the aircraft solo and 17 by the time of licence issue. Additionally, there are seven ground examinations to pass, which require you to study from books and other materials *(most of the exams are multiple choice)*. Alternatively the National Private Pilot's Licence *(NPPL)* is available. The requirements for this are lower *(ie. 32 hours)* and details can be found in the NPPL syllabus.

The theoretical *(ground)* training includes Air Law, Meteorology, Navigation, Flight Planning and Performance, Human Performance, Communications and Aircraft General. You will have to meet certain basic medical standards and obtain a medical certificate before your first solo flight, so it is worth checking that you can pass this before spending large amounts of money on a flying training course. The medical examination has to be carried out with a CAA authorised medical examiner, except for the NPPL, where a GP's certificate is sufficient.

There is a Skill Test to pass at the end of the training which is a handling and navigation test. You will take this test with an approved examiner and there is usually one on the staff of most schools, but you will not be permitted to carry out more than a minimal amount of your training with the examiner.

You will have to budget for items of equipment and study books *(usually not included in the cost of a course)* - often the equipment can be purchased through the school or direct from Pooleys *(address at the back of this book)*. **Exam fees** *(both ground and skill test)* will usually not be included in course prices and will be charged separately.

The total time to complete the course will vary widely depending upon many factors. These include weather and how often you are able to fly. If you were able to fly once per week, for example, you should complete the course within 12 months - but please note that this is a very rough estimate.

If you do not have the time and money to complete the course then think carefully before starting. Learning to fly is much more than an hour or two a week. Commitment and patience are required and a good measure of enthusiasm! Hopefully you will have gone away from your trial lesson with the enthusiasm to learn and to encourage others to fly.

For most people it is a magical experience and we hope that you will have a thoroughly enjoyable trial flying lesson!

Glossary

Aerofoil

The cross section through a wing or tailplane which has a curved upper surface.

Aileron

The hinged surface outboard at the rear of the wing which is used to roll the aircraft around its longitudinal axis.

Altimeter

The instrument used to show the height of the aircraft above a known datum such as the sea or the airfield.

Artificial Horizon

See Attitude Indicator.

ASI

Airspeed Indicator.

ATC

Air Traffic Control.

Attitude Indicator (AI)

An instrument used to show pitch or bank of the aircraft relied upon when the aircraft is in cloud.

Ball

Used to show slip or skid of the aeroplane, and is used to "balance" the aircraft in flight.

Booking Out

The action of obtaining permission or notifying a flight to Air Traffic Control.

CAA

Civil Aviation Authority. The body responsible for the regulation of all flying activities in the UK.

Carb Heat

Abbreviation for carburettor heat. Used to prevent formation of ice in the carburettor.

CFI

Chief Flying Instructor.

Circuit

The traffic pattern around the airfield used to organise the order of landing. Also used to describe the practice of take-offs and landings *("to carry out circuits")*.

Clearance

Permission by Air Traffic Control for an aircraft to taxy, line up on the runway, take off or land.

Coaming

The top of the instrument panel, which is usually a fairly level surface.

Cowling

The panels of the fuselage surrounding the engine.

Cruise

Level flight with a power setting and appropriate mixture setting to achieve best range or fuel economy.

Crosswind

Where the wind is blowing at an angle to the direction of travel during take-off or landing.

Direction Indicator (DI)

The instrument used to show the heading of the aircraft.

Drag

The force produced by the aircraft passing through the air which tends to oppose the motion of the aircraft.

Elevator

The horizontal hinged surface on the rear of the tailplane used to change the pitch attitude.

Final (Approach)

The last sector of the circuit when the aircraft is coming in to land and is lined up with the runway.

Flaps

Hinged sections attached inboard to the rear of the wing which can be lowered to assist the take-off or the landing.

Hold or Holding Point

An area close to the runway where the pilot will carry out power checks and pre take-off checks.

JAR

Joint Airworthiness Requirements *(a set of rules agreed by a number of European States to encourage harmonisation of aviation matters between the member states).*

Knot (kt)

The speed of one nautical mile per hour.

Lift

The upward force produced by the flow of air over an aerofoil.

Mixture Control

Used to adjust the fuel/air ratio to the carburettor for maximum fuel efficiency.

NAV

Navigation.

PIC

Pilot in Command.

Pitch

The rotation of the aeroplane around its lateral *(wingtip-to-wingtip)* axis.

PPL

Private Pilots Licence.

PTT

Press to talk - the transmit button for the radio.

PU/T

Pilot under training - a student pilot.

QFE

The subscale setting on the altimeter so that the altimeter shows the height of the aircraft above the airfield.

QNH

The subscale setting on the altimeter so that the altimeter shows the altitude above sea level.

Roll

The rotation of the aeroplane around its longitudinal *(nose-to-tail)* axis.

Rudder

The vertical hinged surface on the rear of the tailfin used to assist in turning the aircraft left or right and to prevent unwanted yaw.

Stall

The condition which occurs when an aerofoil ceases to create sufficient lift due to an excessively high angle between the aerofoil and the relative airflow.

"Ts and Ps"

Engine oil Temperature and Pressure gauges used to assess the health of the engine.

Tach. or Tachometer

A dial showing in revolutions per minute (rpm) how fast the engine and propeller are turning.

Taxy

The action of moving the aircraft along the ground with engine power.

Tec or Tech Log

Technical log - used to record all the flights of a specific aircraft.

Threshold

The beginning of the runway.

Thrust

The forward force created by the propeller.

Throttle

The lever used to select the rpm.

Trim Wheel or Trimmer

A device to relieve forward and backwards pressure on the control column reducing the workload of the pilot and enabling the aircraft to be flown "hands off".

Turn Co-ordinator

An instrument showing the rate of turn of the aircraft. The glass tube fitted with a ball shows slip and skid (yaw).

Vertical Speed Indicator (VSI)

Vertical Speed Indicator - shows rate of climb or descent.

Yaw

The rotation of the aeroplane around its normal *(top-to-bottom)* axis.

Phonetic Alphabet

A	Alpha		**N**	November
B	Bravo		**O**	Oscar
C	Charlie		**P**	Papa
D	Delta		**Q**	Quebec
E	Echo		**R**	Romeo
F	Foxtrot		**S**	Sierra
G	Golf		**T**	Tango
H	Hotel		**U**	Uniform
I	India		**V**	Victor
J	Juliet		**W**	Whiskey
K	Kilo		**X**	X-Ray
L	Lima		**Y**	Yankee
M	Mike		**Z**	Zulu

Useful Addresses

Aeronautical Information Service (AIS)
National Air Traffic Services Ltd
Control Tower Building
Heathrow Airport
Hounslow
Middlesex TW6 1JJ
Tel: 020 8745 3456
e-mail: ais.supervisor@nats.co.uk
website: http://www.ais.org.uk

Air League
The Broadway House
Tothill Street
London SW1H 9NS
Tel: 020 7222 8463
e-mail: exec@airleague.co.uk
website: http://www.airleague.co.uk

Aircraft Owners and Pilots Association (AOPA)
50a Cambridge Street
London SW1V 4QQ
Tel: 020 7834 5631
e-mail: aopa@easynet.co.uk
website: http://www.aopa.co.uk

British Microlight Aircraft Association (BMAA)
Bullring, Deddington, Banbury
Oxon OX15 0TT
Tel: 01869 338888
e-mail: general@bmaa.org

website: http://www.bmaa.org
British Women Pilots Association (BWPA)
Brooklands Museum
Weybridge KT13 0QN
e-mail: enquiries@bwpa.demon.co.uk
website: http://www.bwpa.demon.co.uk

Civil Aviation Authority Safety Regulation Group (CAA)
Aviation House
South Area
Gatwick Airport
West Sussex RH6 0YR
Tel: 01293 567171 (Switchboard);
573700 (Licensing); 573685 (Medical)
Website: http://www.caa.co.uk

General Aviation Safety Council (GASCO)
Rochester Airport
Chatham
Kent ME5 9SD
Tel: 01634 200203
e-mail: info@gasco.uk.net
website: http://www.gasco.org.uk

Guild of Air Pilots and Air Navigators (GAPAN)
Cobham House
9 Warwick Court
London WC1R 5DJ
Tel: 020 7404 4032
e-mail: gapan@gapan.org
website: http://www.gapan.org

Pooleys Flight Equipment Ltd
Elstree Aerodrome, Herts WD6 3AW
Tel: 020 8953 4870
Fax: 020 8953 2512
e-mail: sales@pooleys.com
Website: http://www.pooleys.com

Popular Flying Association (PFA)
Turweston Aerodrome, Nr Brackley,
Northants NN13 5YD
Tel: 01280 846786
e-mail: office@pfa.org.uk
website: http://www.pfa.org.uk

Royal Aero Club of the United Kingdom (RAeC)
Kimberley House, Vaughan Way, Leceister LE1 4SG
Tel: 0116 2531 1051
Fax: 0116 2531 5939
e-mail: secretary@royalaeroclub.org
website: http://www.royalaeroclub.org

Royal Aeronautical Society
4 Hamilton Place, London W1J 7BQ
Tel: 020 7499 3515
Fax: 020 7499 6230
Website: http://www.aerosociety.com

Useful Websites

www.pilotweb.co.uk   (Pilot Magazine)
www.flyer.co.uk   (Flyer Magazine)
www.todayspilot.co.uk   (Today's Pilot Magazine)

A Great Fixed-Wing Pilot's Starter Kit from Pooleys to get you into the Air

This pack contains the following items:

1. APM Volume 1, 2, 3, 4, 6 and 7.
2. PPL Confuser.
3. Pooleys Loose Leaf Flight Guide
   (complete with annual amendments) latest edition.
4. Pooleys NM-2 Scale Ruler.
5. Pooleys PP-1 Protractor.
6. Pooleys CRP-1 Computer.
7. Pooleys CB-2 Kneeboard & Log Pad.
8. Pooleys PPL Log Book.
9. Set of non-permanent Lumocolour Markers.
10. CAA 1:500,000 chart of your local area *(please specify area required)*.
11. Large Courier Case.

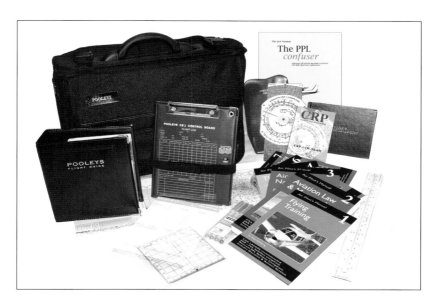

Certificate of Completion
of an Aeroplane

Trial Flying Lesson

This is to certify that

----

has piloted an aeroplane on their own under the
guidance of a qualified flying instructor, and has
successfully completed:

Instructor (QFI) ---

Date ---